Tripawd Jackson

Three-Legged Hero

Written by Karis R. Lowrie

Illustrations By: Abigail Roscoe

Published by Tripawd Books

Table of Contents

This book is dedicated to my nieces and nephews;
Esther, Judah, Billy, Margot, and Emma.
And to the newest addition to the family,
we may not know who you are now, but we are
so excited to welcome you into the family.

This book is also dedicated to the best dog and cat
anyone could ever have asked for, to my Tripawd Jackson
and Miracle. You have been with me through all the hard
times and all the times of joy. I am so grateful to have
rescued you both, as you both have helped me in return.

Finally, this book is dedicated to all the
amazing wildlife rehabilitators,
whose efforts are often overlooked by
the general community but greatly
appreciated by the animals you care for.
For all of your hard work
and dedication, we thank you.

Meet Jackson

Everyone is unique. Every animal is different. Some animals are cold blooded, some animals are warm blooded. Some animals fly, some swim, and some animals walk on four legs.

Hello, my name is Tripawd Jackson and I have three legs. I was born with four, but one of my legs was injured when I was just a puppy. At first, I didn't trust anyone. I didn't know what to do. I was all alone, scared, and in pain.

My new mother found me and adopted me. She brought me home to live with her and my new older brother named Miracle. He is a grey tabby cat. He was also injured when he was young, but my mother found him and saved him too. My mother took me to many veterinarians to try to save my leg, but it couldn't be fixed. So, my leg was amputated so that I would not hurt anymore. Without the leg, I am no longer afraid and no longer in pain.

I am happy being a tripawd. I like to run and play with my friends and family.
I enjoy chasing the chickens, and I love to ride in the boat.

My mother helps me get around on three legs. I have a special blue vest I wear
when we go out so she can help me when I need it. Sometimes I stumble and
fall, but my mom is always
there to get me back up again.

My family does everything together. We have traveled to and have lived in
many different places. We have gone for long car rides across many states.
We have hiked out to see huge glaciers. We have been swimming in deep oceans.

I have a very important job.
 I work with my mother who is a Wildlife Rehabilitator. She takes care of
injured and orphaned animals at a wildlife hospital.
My mother and I are specially trained to handle and assist wildlife. Mother
uses special gloves and other equipment when coming into contact with wildlife.
I love helping other animals in need.
I remember what it was like to be scared and in pain, so I want to help others

in the same situation. Mother and I work hard to save everyone we can.

Opossum in Peril

I enjoy my morning hikes with my mother. Sometimes we climb tall mountains, sometimes we walk through big fields of flowers, and sometimes we cross strong rivers.

There are a lot of things to see, sounds to hear, and scents to smell when we go hiking. One of my favorite spots is the glacier.

The air temperature around us is warm and comfortable. The ground is cold and covered in ice and snow. There are beautiful caves made of ice and freezing rivers flowing out from under our feet. Mother and I go hiking wherever we travel.

One time, we were out on a trail in the forest, and I smelled a strange smell.

I followed that new smell and I found a Virginia opossum with an injured foot. Opossums are a type of animal called a marsupial. They have a pouch where they carry their babies. This opossum was a mama carrying her eleven babies in her pouch.

Her babies were very small, about the size of jellybeans. My mother wrapped the opossum in her jacket, and we brought her and the babies to the wildlife hospital to treat her injured foot.

Mother set up a nice warm place for her to stay while her foot healed.
I kept a close eye on the opossum to make sure she was safe.

We gave her lots of warm blankets.
In the wild, an opossum will use her prehensile tail to carry
leaves to make her bed. At the hospital, mama opossum used her
tail to make her bed out of the soft blankets. She stayed with us
for a long time. Eventually the babes came out of her pouch,
ready to see the world around them.
They clung to mama to keep them safe.

After a few weeks of rest, she was feeling a lot better. Then my mother,
the mama opossum, the babies, and myself all went out to the hiking trail
where we had found her. My mother gently set mama opossum down and
she walked off carrying her babies with her. She was very happy to be back
home where she belongs. The babies were excited to see the new environment arour
them.
As they trotted off into the woods, mother and I finished our hike and headed back
home.

Did you know?

- Opossums can eat about 5,000 ticks per season.
- Opossums are immune to Lyme disease and some other tick-born illnesses.
- Opossums are also immune to rabies because their body temperature is too low.
- Opossums have fifty teeth.

Going Gosling

I like to help out on the farm. One of my jobs is to herd the chickens and keep them safe. It is a big responsibility to look after them. I watch out for potential dangers in the area and I make sure the chickens stay out of the pond. I have to keep them all together, so I know
where they all are.

One day I was out in the field watching the flock when I heard a small cry.

I tried to figure out who was crying. Neither the hens nor the rooster was crying. The crying was coming from the river. I gathered my flock and brought them with me. At the river I found a little gosling, which is a baby goose.

The gosling had no parents and no siblings. He was all alone. I called my mother over to help. She gently picked up the baby and wrapped it in a soft towel. We needed to find a new home for the gosling. He was too young to be alone.

He couldn't live with the chickens. He couldn't live with the cows.
He needed a family of geese to live with.

12

Mother cared for the gosling while I looked everywhere for the right family. I searched every tree in the woods. I checked around the haybales in the field.

I looked in old logs, under mossy rocks, and all around the garden. Finally, I headed over to the pond. Right there in the water I saw them. A mother and a father goose and three little goslings just about the same age as our little one.

I brought my mother and our gosling out to the pond to show them what I'd found. My mother gently put him down next to the pond. When the mama goose saw our gosling, she called over to him. Our baby was so excited. He jumped in the water and swam out to them as fast as he could. The other babies were very curious about the new addition.

The goose family adopted our little gosling. Mother and I watched the new family swim around the pond for a while. Then we went back to our home. I still see the goose family swim in the pond every day—the mother and the father geese, and their four little goslings.

Did you know?

- Male and female geese have different vocalizations.
- Geese have a lifespan of around 10-25 years in the wild.
- Some types of geese have a serrated edge on their beaks called tomia.
- Asian bar-headed geese regularly fly over the Himalayan Mountains at an altitude of over 30,000 ft.

14

Who's there?

The other day, I was playing hide-and-go-seek with my mother in the back field. I love playing that game. My mother hides and I search for her. This time it was difficult to find her.

I had just finished looking behind all the haybales when I heard a phone ring. I followed the ringing and found the phone, and my mother, hiding in a tree. I was so excited that I'd found her and won the game. My mother climbed down and answered her phone. She talked for a while. When she finished her call, she told me we were going to go for a car ride. I love riding in the car! We got in the car and drove for a long time.

Finally, we stopped at a large brick building. It had huge windows and lots of lights all around it. My mother and I got out of the car and went to the front door. There was a tall man there standing next to a box. Inside the box was a tiny little owl. It was not a baby owl, but a small adult. The man said that the little owl had been looking for food when it flew into one of the big windows of the building. My mother and I drove the little owl to the wildlife hospital.

My mother looked over the owl to see if he was injured. She checked his wings, she checked his beak, she checked his feet, and she checked his eyes. The little owl's wings were ok, his beak and his feet were fine, but mother said his eyes were injured. The owl was blind; he could not see.

We kept the owl at our hospital for a while hoping that his eyesight would come back, but it did not. In the wild, owls use their eyes to search for food and to avoid predators. This little owl could not be released if he could not see. So my mother made a lot of phone calls and talked to a lot of people until she found a new home for the little owl.

We all got into the car: my mother, the owl, and I. We drove to the zoo. A very nice zookeeper was there to meet us. He said he had the perfect home for our little owl.

He would be given food because he couldn't find it on his own, he would have a nice shelter to keep him safe, and he would have lots of fun toys to keep him busy. He was going to love his new home. The zookeeper also said our owl would be an animal ambassador. He would help teach children who visit the zoo about owls and their environment.

My mother thanked the man and we went back home.

A few days later my mother brought me back to check on our little owl. He is very happy. He likes to teach the children, he likes to eat his food, and he loves to play with his toys. He is very happy being an animal ambassador.

Did you know?
- Some owls are nocturnal; they are awake at night.
- Some owls are crepuscular; they are awake during the dawn and dusk.
- Owls can rotate their heads very far around, about 270°.
- Owls cannot roll their eyes like we can, because their eyes are shaped like cones.

Caribou Lost

After my mother adopted me, I got a lot of new family members.
I got my mother and my brother, Miracle.
I also got new aunts, uncles, cousins, and grandparents.
There are always a lot of children, dogs, and cats running around
the house to play with. When my mother wants to get my attention,
she uses a special whistle to call me. That's how I know it's her.
If I'm out playing with the other dogs, she can call me in and I
know she is calling for me.

One day, I went hiking with my mother.
We climbed up a tall mountain and crossed over a small stream.
We arrived at a little field without any trees.

In the field was a baby caribou all by itself.
The little caribou was scared and hungry. She ran right up to us.
In the wild, mother deer might leave their babies hidden for a while,
then return to them later. But when a baby deer approaches strangers,
it may need help. This little caribou had lost its family.

My mother and I looked for the herd, with the baby caribou following behind. Every time she took a step her little hooves made a "click clack" noise. We walked a few yards then "click clack click clack" the baby followed behind. We couldn't see the caribou herd, and I couldn't smell them but we had to
keep searching.

We decided to take a break and rest for a while. Even while we were lying down, I could still hear a quiet "click clack" sound. Then I heard more -- "click clack, click clack!" I got up and ran toward the direction of the noise—and discovered an entire herd of caribou: mothers, fathers, aunts, uncles,
brothers, and sisters.

I turned around to see if my mother and the baby caribou had followed me, but I couldn't see them.
Then I heard my mother's whistle. She was calling for me. I ran back to her and then brought them both over to the herd. The baby caribou was very happy to be back with her family, and I was happy
to be with my mother.

Did you know?

- Caribou shed their antlers and regrow them each year.
- Both the males and the females will grow antlers, but they shed them at different times.
- It is thought that the popping "click clack" sound that the caribou make when they walk is meant to help the herd stay together.
- If you find a baby deer hiding in the grass; leave it be, keep an eye on it, and contact your local wildlife center to ask for advice. Often times the best option is to leave it alone and the mother will return.

Broken Box Turtle

 I love riding in the boat. I enjoy watching the fish swimming under the water. I sav◌
the smell the crisp clean air, and I like listening to the gulls calling out to each othe◌

We see lots of different fish and many types of aquatic turtles while we are out ◌
the lake. Sometimes I swim in the calm water. My mother uses my special vest ◌
help me stay above the water.
We have so much fun out on the water.

One day we were getting ready to go for a boat ride. I was so excited!
Mother got the boat trailer hooked up to the car and we were off. We drove for ◌
little while and were almost at the lake, when my mother saw something up ahea◌
and stopped the car suddenly.

We got out and a few feet away we saw a turtle. He was a Woodland Box Turtle, ◌
type of terrestrial turtle. The turtle had a crack in his shell. He had been crossin◌
the road when he was struck by a car.

My mother carefully put the turtle in a box, and we all got in our car. Mother turned the car around, and we drove to the wildlife hospital. My mother helped the veterinarian bandage the turtle's shell. We set up a comfy place for the turtle to recover.

It took a long time for him to recover. Mother and the wildlife hospital team took turns caring for the turtle. They kept his wound clean and dry. I kept watch over the little turtle, making sure he stayed safe while in our care.

Finally, his shell was fully healed. We drove him back to the area where we found him and let him go—far away from the road. He went on his way, happy to be in the warm sunny grass. Then mother and I finally went for our boat ride. As we went out on the water, I felt proud of our accomplishment and what we had done to save that little turtle.

Did you know?

• Male box turtles have red eyes. Females have golden brown eyes.

• Box turtles, like other turtles, can live for a long time. Their average lifespan is fifty years.

• Some turtles are aquatic and spend most of their life in the water.

• Some turtles, like box turtles, are terrestrial and live most of their life on land.

What can you do to help?

Jackson loves to help his mother in wildlife rehabilitation.
He knows what his role is during a rescue and he understands how
he can best assist the wildlife hospital team. It is very important to
remember that injured and orphaned wildlife need to be treated by
 trained professionals. In many cases, it is illegal for the public to be
in possession of these animals.

The best option for the animal's survival is to find a local certified wildlife
rehabilitator or wildlife rehabilitation center.

 Most centers have a phone line you can call if you are unsure whether
the animal needs help or not.
If you are unable to find a wildlife rehabilitator,
you can contact your local governing wildlife agency.

28

So How Can *YOU* Help Wildlife?

Be sure to have an adult assist you with these options:

1. If you find a wild animal you believe to be injured or orphaned, contact your local wildlife center.

2. If your family has birdfeeders in your yard, be sure to regularly wash and sanitize them.

3. If you have large open windows in your house, ask your adults if you can place stickers or hang pictures to prevent bird strikes.

4. Donate animal food, cleaning products, pet bowls, and other products to your local wildlife rehab center. Many centers will provide a list of needed items. You can fundraise to earn money for the center as well.

5. Ask your local wildlife center if they accept volunteers.

6. Plant native wildflowers and other native plants in your garden.

7. Look into assisting with local bird or butterfly counts, or other wildlife counts.

8. Ask your local wildlife center or zoo about other ways in which you can help.

Remember, only a trained professional or those directed by a certified professional should attempt to capture, restrain, or in any other way come into contact with wildlife.

Glossary

1. **Amputation** - removing a part of the body (e.g. Jackson's leg was amputated)
2. **Animal ambassador** - an animal not able to be released into the wild, who helps to educate the public about their wild counterparts
3. **Aquatic** - living in the water (e.g. aquatic turtles, like snapping turtles)
4. **Crepuscular** - animals who are awake during dawn and dusk
5. **Environment** - the area and everything around where an animal lives (e.g. Some snakes live in a dessert environment while others can live in a mostly aquatic environment or in a forest environment.)
6. **Gosling** - a baby goose
7. **Glacier** - a slow-moving frozen body of water
8. **Lyme disease** - a serious illness transmitted by tick bites
9. **Marsupial** - a mammal who carries their young in a pouch
10. **Nocturnal** - animals who are awake during the night
11. **Prehensile tail** - an animal tail which is able to be used as an appendage (like an extra hand or a foot)
12. **Rabies** - a dangerous illness transmitted through some animal bites
13. **Serrated** - jagged or rough (e.g. Some geese have a serrated edge on their beaks.)
14. **Terrestrial** - living on land (e.g. Terrestrial turtles, like box turtles)
15. **Tomia** - the serrated edge of some birds' beaks
16. **Tripawd** - an animal with three legs, usually because of amputation.
17. **Veterinarian** - a licensed doctor who cares for animals at a veterinary clinic.
18. **Vocalizations** - calls or sounds made by an animal (e.g. The vocalization of a goose is normally expressed as a "honk".)
19. **Wildlife hospital** - a veterinary hospital focusing on the care of wildlife
20. **Wildlife rehabilitator** - a trained professional who cares for wildlife with the goal of release

About Tripawd Jackson

Jackson is a hound mix. He was less than six months old when he was badly injured by his previous owner. He ended up with six different fractures in his leg. He could not use his leg and was in a lot of pain. He was being cared for at a shelter that was not able to properly treat his injuries. He was passed up for adoption by multiple people because of his potential medical costs and because he was very afraid.

Karis had been looking for a special needs dog who would get along with her older special needs cat, Miracle. Thankfully she found Jackson and adopted him. She brought him home and immediately started his veterinary care. Jackson and Karis consulted with multiple veterinarians regarding his leg. At this time, Jackson was afraid of everything and would not allow anyone to pet him.

With the recommendation from the veterinarians, it was decided the best option for Jackson was to amputate the injured leg. Shortly after the amputation, Jackson's personality changed for the better. He was no longer in pain and no longer afraid of everything. He started to enjoy being around people and letting them pet him. Today Jackson is a happy dog who loves to play. He loves to go hiking and ride in the family boat, and he gets along great hopping on three legs.

About Karis Lowrie

Karis is a certified wildlife rehabilitator. She has a degree in Zoology and several years of training in wildlife rehab. She has experience caring for a wide variety of native North American wildlife including hoof stock, rabies vector species, other small mammals, raptors, waterfowl, songbirds, reptiles, and amphibians.

She also has experience working in wildlife education and conservation. Karis strives to help wildlife and humans coexist by informing the public about native wildlife. Her passion is to help animals in need.

Jackson and Karis

Made in the USA
Monee, IL
02 June 2020